Illustrated, written, and conceived by Haidee Soule Merritt

Additional copies available from:
Bird Wing Press
155 Cabot Street, Portsmouth, NH 03801 USA
www.haideemerritt.com

ISBN13: 978-0-9822561-0-7

Book design and production: Grace Peirce
www.nhmuse.com

The contents of this book, such as text and graphics are for informational purposes only. The Content is not intended as a substitute for professional medical advice, diagnosis, or treatment. Always seek the advice of your physician or other qualified health provider with any questions you may have regarding a medical condition. Never disregard professional medical advice or delay in seeking it because of Content found here!!!

There's no doubt I'm a late bloomer (I overheard my Mom saying so to my first boyfriend). Although I'm not opposed to embracing a trend, you can *be* pretty darn sure it's no longer cool by the time I get wind of it. I live in New Hampshire, for godssake: I don't really even try.

However, I am riding high atop the latest craze, proud as punch to be on the cutting edge for once. I have been a Type I diabetic longer than my memories go back; one of the originals, you might say. Lord knows, you can't throw a rock without hitting a diabetic these days, you really can't. Type I, Type 2, and all the in-betweens they're so fond of labeling us with. It's not just me; everybody's SOME type of diabetic. Hell, it's the new trend.

In case you haven't heard, diabetes isn't just a disease, it's a lifestyle. I've been living it long enough to know it sucks. If you think it's easy—you know, "just watch your diet"—then you're not doing it right. I've put my complaints to paper (a lot more paper than you're holding right now, by the way) although I can't quite remember why I started. Maybe I thought my dark sense of humor would pay off someday, somehow? So, thanks for helping me out: if you've got a few minutes, grab a seat and let me enlighten you...

What Sucks About Being Diabetic?

Bruises...

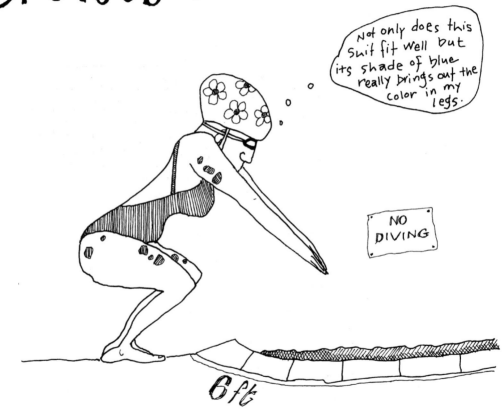

Moodiness...

buffet, *n.* a diabetic's idea of "Self-Help."

buffets...

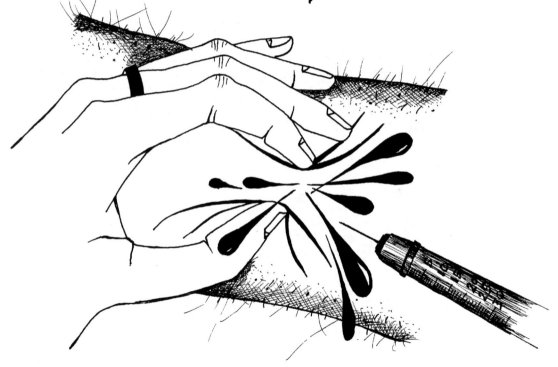

Low blood sugar after sex...

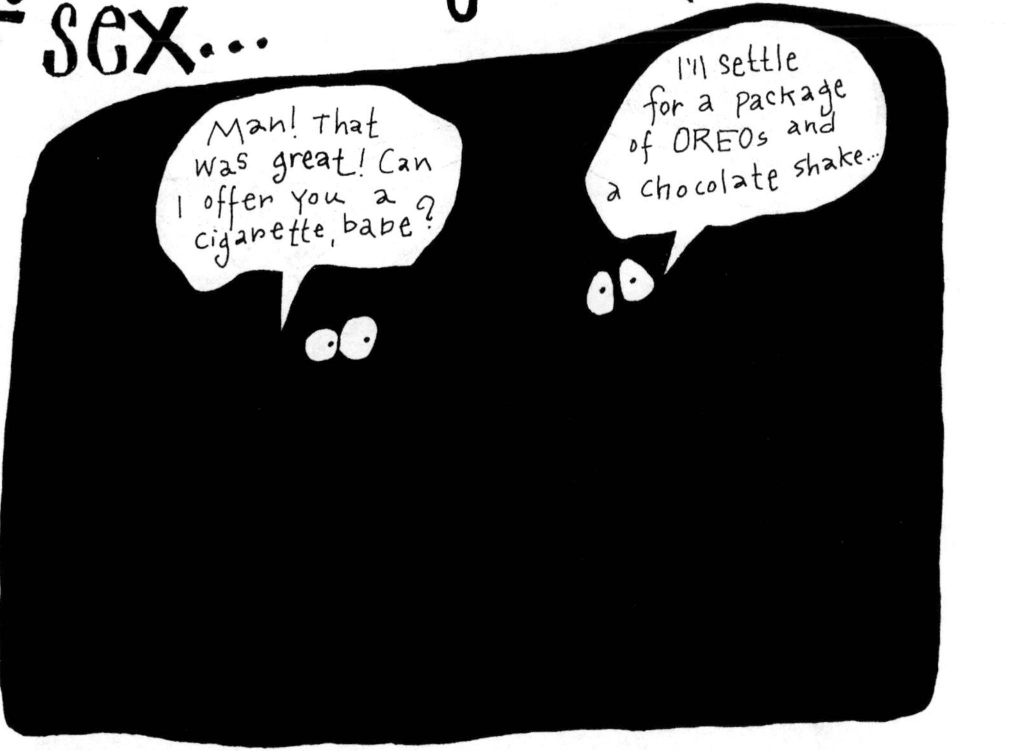

There are <u>NO</u> small injuries...

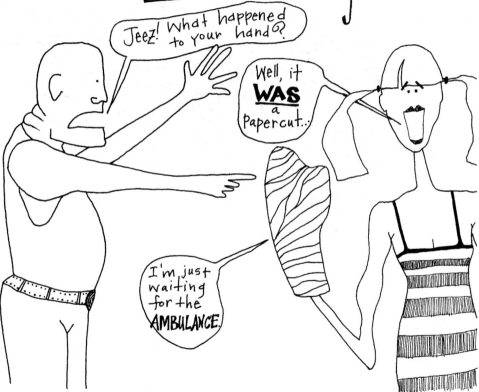

Gifts of food...

people watch you too closely...

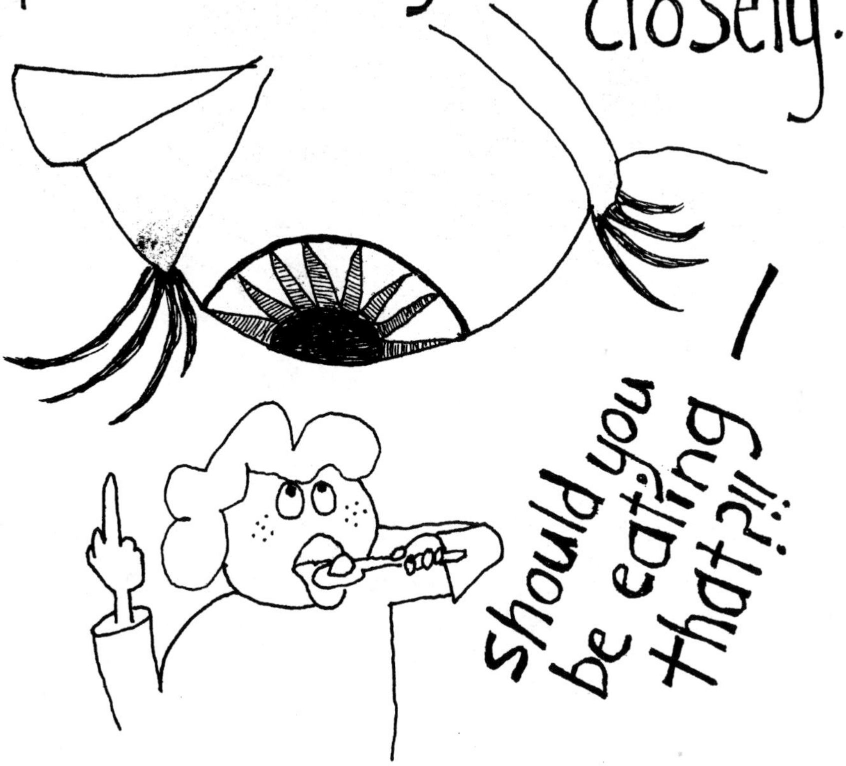

...dishonesty...

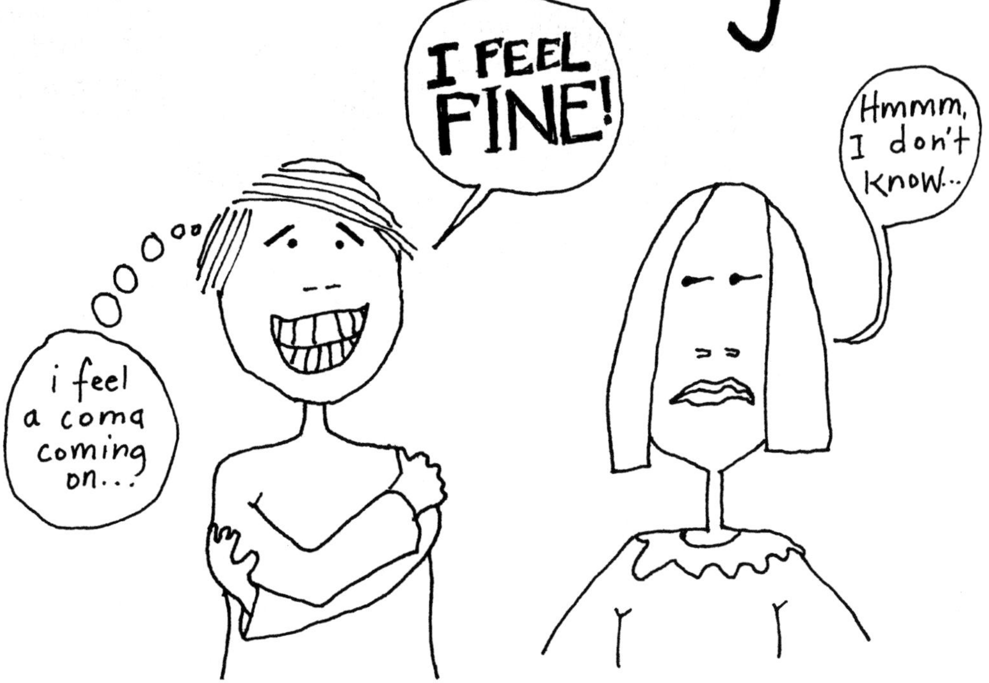

...dishonesty...

cross-ies

...and more dishonesty...

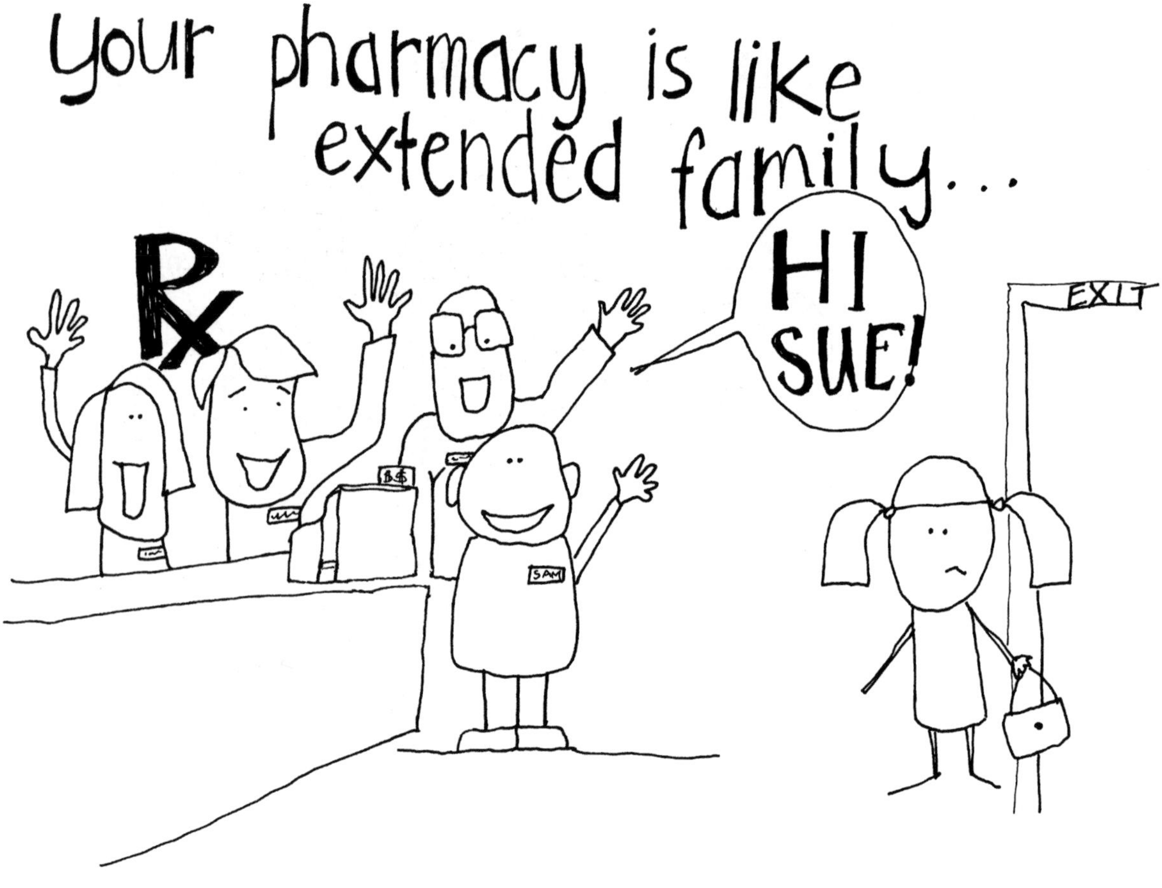
your pharmacy is like extended family...
Rx
HI SUE!
SAM
EXIT

glucose testing...
I don't even know how we lived without blood meters
The #s can really make or break your DAY!
I have callouses on all my finger tips !!!
I would rather leave my house without my ARMS, quite frankly.

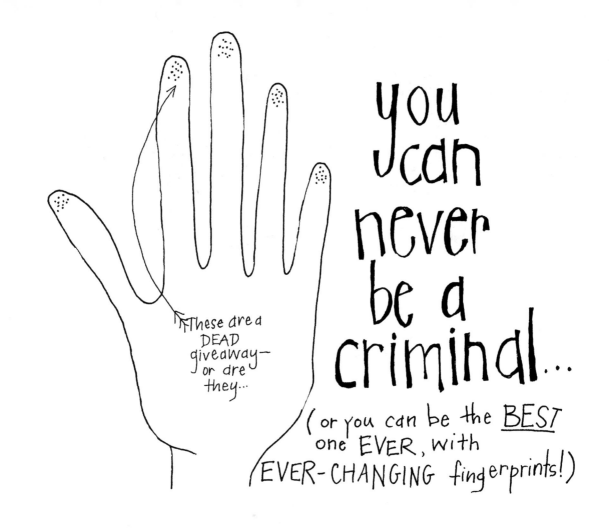

...plus you leave a trail
of DNA as evidence...

pills enough to
fill a candydish...

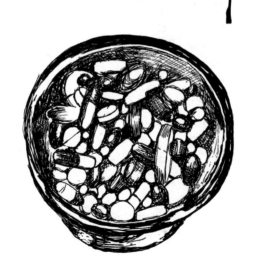

Whoopie Pies...

whoopee!
YOU
CAN'T
HAVE 'EM!

cheating...

I know this will really make me feel crappy — but I'm going to eat it anyway!
why do we still do it???

getting caught...
Hi honey! I'm home EARLY!
shit.
COOKIE JAR
oh, the shame!

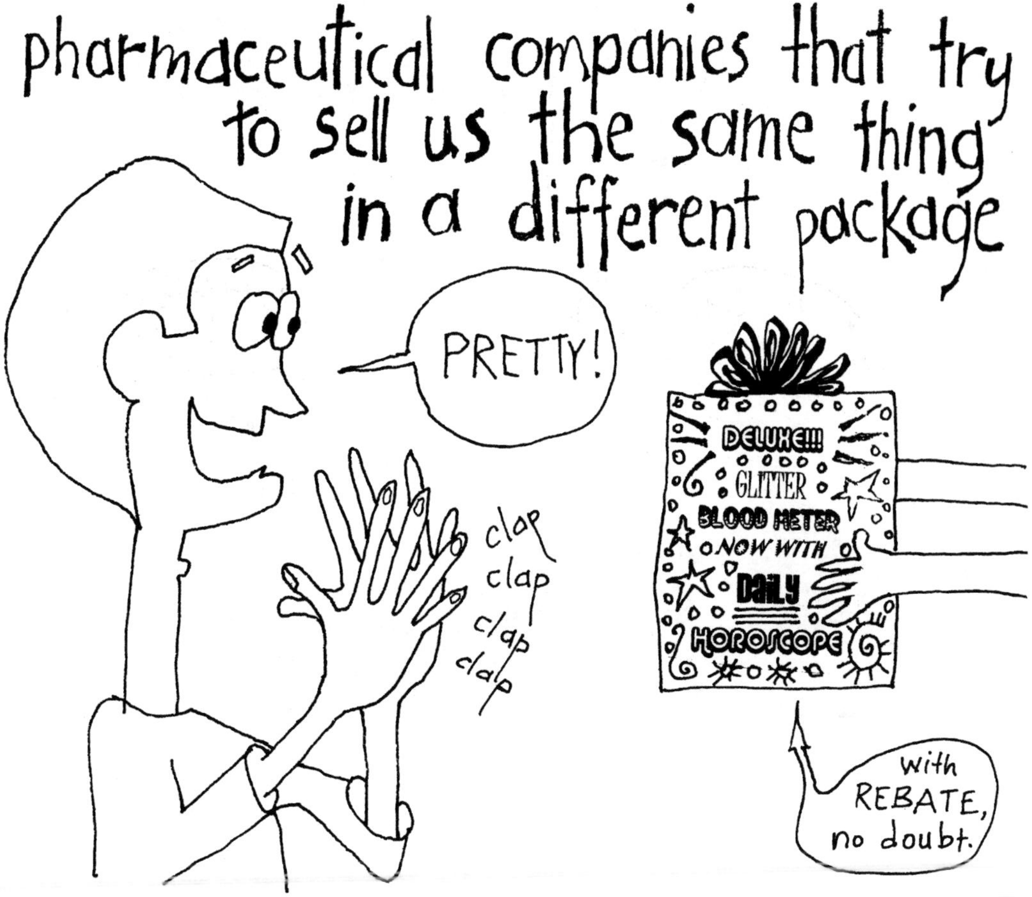
pharmaceutical companies that try to sell us the same thing in a different package
PRETTY!
clap clap clap clap
DELUXE!!!
GLITTER
BLOOD METER
NOW WITH
DAILY
HOROSCOPE
with REBATE, no doubt.

Blood gets all over everything...

(especially if it's important, naturally)

NOTE: Use your imagine-ation and pretend this is red.

brief moments of elation...

and depression...

PANIC...

BUT WORSE

other people's panic...

Walk-a-thons...

It's a full-time job you're <u>not</u> paid for...

it's hard to raise money for research because we don't look "SICK"...

social stigmas...

tough l♡ve...

The first word in a diabetic's vocabulary.

Late dinners...

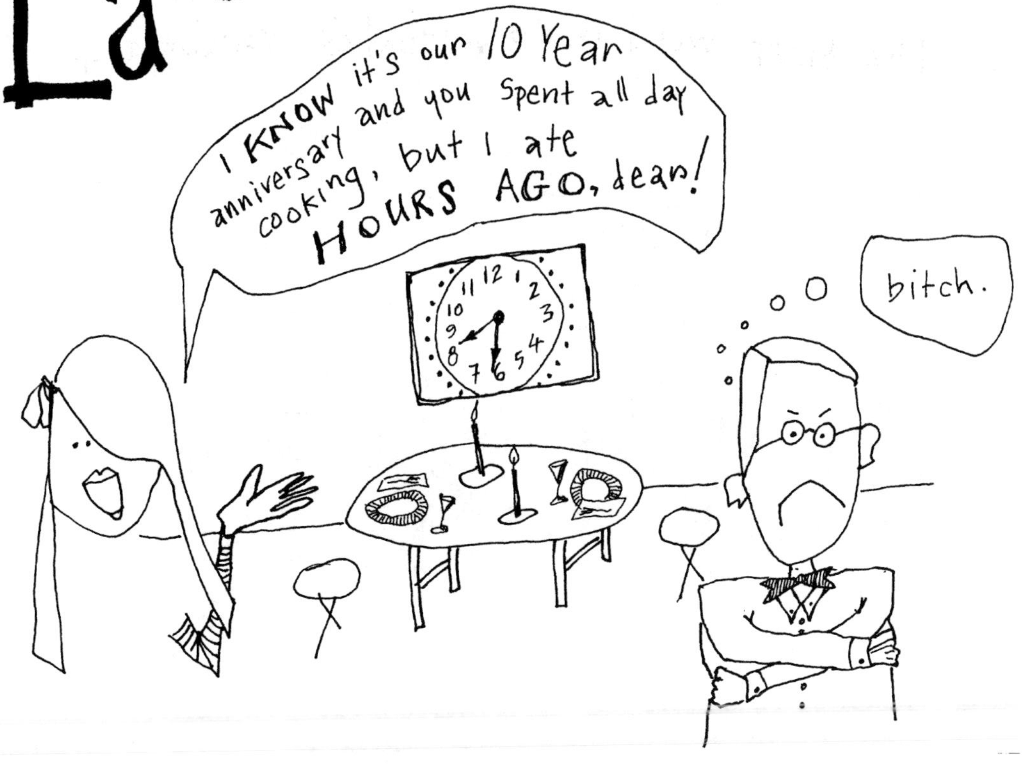

new gadgets mix it up a little...

BUT—

(dramatic pause)

Insulin is
NOT
a cure, folks...

artificial sweeteners...

fingerpricks...

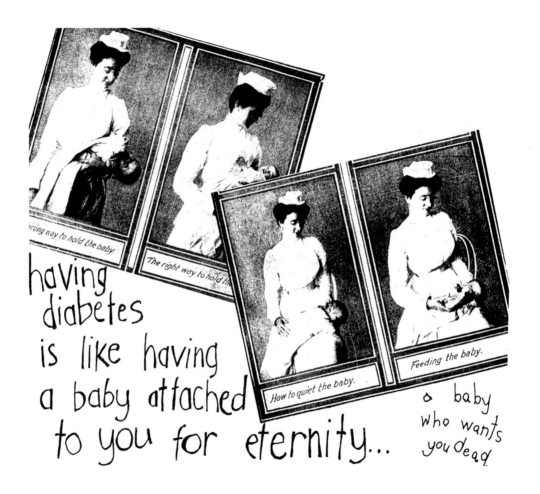

having
diabetes
is like having
a baby attached
to you for eternity...
a baby
who wants
you dead

babies don't arrive with an
instruction manual

and neither do diabetics...

...but <u>one</u> doesn't grow up and leave home...

piñatas...

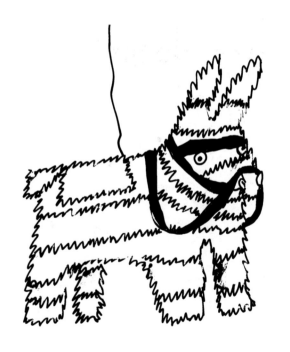

Q: what diabetic kid doesn't want candy to fall from the sky?

A: what parent will buy one for their diabetic kid?

mosquitos love you...

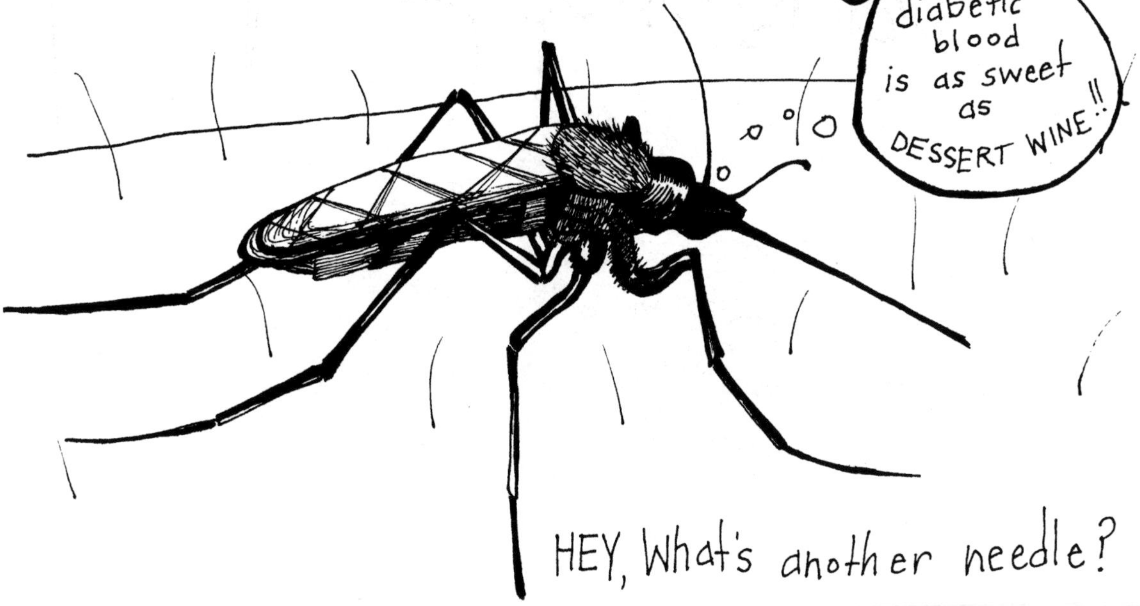

HEY, What's another needle?

you feel quite at liberty to pick your
NOSE...
I feel quite at liberty to do this.

oh wait...
apparently that's
just me...

eating disorders...

Diabetes, by *definition*, should be an eating disorder.

Seriously, it's a can of worms I'm just not prepared to open right here.

your feet aren't warm for months...

Even under 6 pairs of socks.

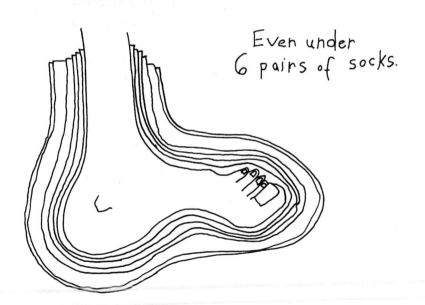

ketostix ™

98%
of the time
you piss on
your own
HAND

Denial...

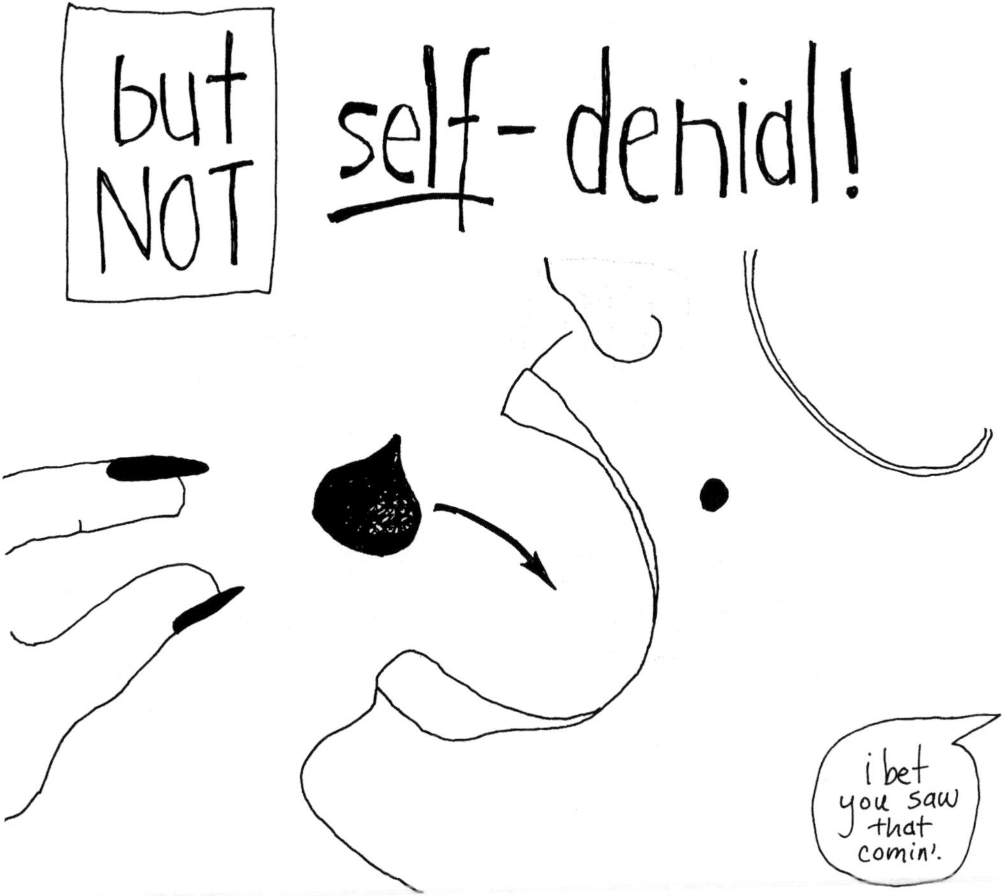

but NOT
self-denial!
i bet you saw that comin'.

primitive treatment...

Hey, this is recent history, folks. Until the introduction of synthetic insulin in 1982, we injected the insulin we harvested from our barnyard friends, the Pig and the cow.

(How curious that I'm a lactose-intolerant vegetarian.)

chronic skin issues...

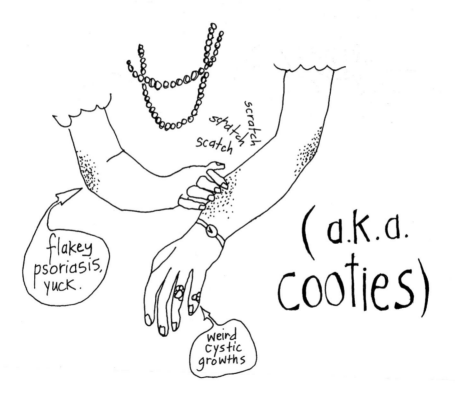

(a.k.a. cooties)

limp dicks...
It's called ERECTILE DYSFUNCTION.
Yeah, whatever never thought I'd be thankful to be a diabetic woman!

poor dental health...

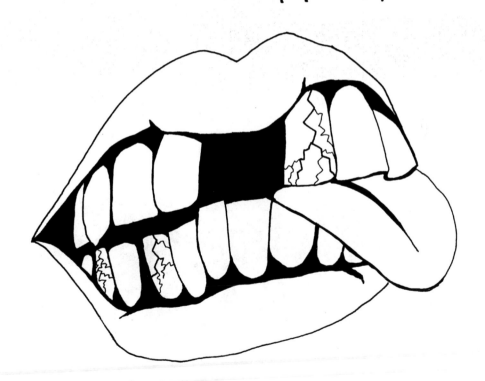

carpal tunnel...

Corporal Tunnel reporting for duty.

Alternative Medicine

?

Diabetic Sleeping Pill :

Painkillers:

Diabetic
Anti-Depressants:

(plain or peanut)

Band-Aid

a few hints...

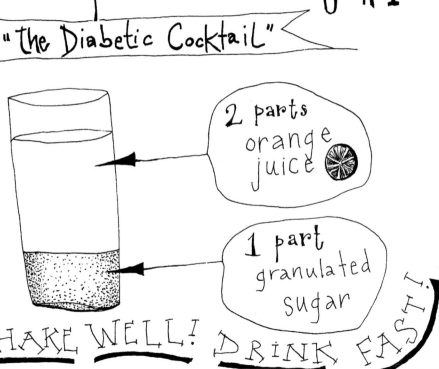

sometimes
i add VODKA

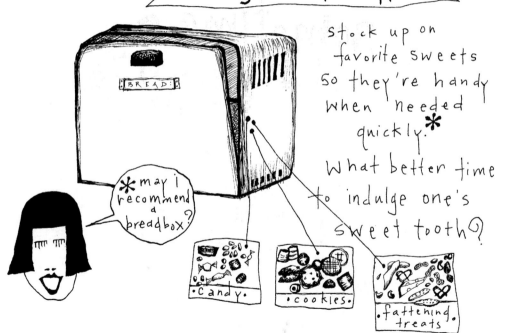

Hypoglycemia Hint #3

Learn to manipulate fast-acting
insulin to peak at
optimal times...

Yum! Yum!

... like the arrival of
the DESSERT CART !!

HYPOGLYCEMIA HINT #4

never enter
into an argument
(especially with a
loved one) while

experiencing symptoms
of low blood sugar...

you may devour your enemy
in more ways than one!

...and live to regret it!!!

beware
my
Wrath!!

I'm sure your diabetes sucks too.
Save your energy for those who understand:
Mail your complaint(s) to:

H.S. Merritt
155 Cabot Street
Portsmouth, NH 03801
haidee@haideemerritt.com